This
kindl
by th
2016.

Secret in the Shadows

Tony Bradman ■ Jonatronix

OXFORD

Chapter 1 – A living legend

Deep underground at NASTI, Dr X grimaced as images of Max, Cat, Ant and Tiger flashed before him on the plasma screen. He muttered and tutted to himself. Just behind him, Plug and Socket looked at each other nervously. They'd seen their boss in a mood like this before.

"Er, boss …" said Plug, shifting anxiously from foot to foot.

"BE QUIET!" yelled Dr X. "This could be important!" His eyes didn't move from the screen.

The pictures were being beamed from Dr X's spy-bot. The four friends hadn't noticed the two little eyes watching them. They were too busy listening to their head teacher, Mrs Mills, talking about this year's school trip.

Dr X suddenly went quite still. Then a sinister smile inched slowly across his face.

He turned around and looked at Plug and Socket. They gulped and took a hasty step backwards. They'd seen this look before and it only meant one thing …

"So, it seems our four friends are going to Loch Ness," said Dr X. "I've got a brilliant idea! A plan so good that even you two blundering buffoons can't ruin it."

Plug and Socket exchanged hurt looks. They didn't like it when Dr X called them names, especially when it involved words like *blundering* or *bumbling* or Dr X's particular favourite – *ninnies*!

"Actually, my plan is *so* amazing people will be talking about me for years to come," said Dr X dreamily, lost in his imagination. "I'll be a living legend."

Dr X liked the idea of being famous – an infamous villain. "No more hiding underground for me," he boomed.

"Er … it won't be dangerous, will it, Boss?" asked Plug. Dr X's ideas rarely worked out well for his two henchmen.

"Dangerous? Ha ha, of course not!" laughed Dr X, snapping back into the real world. "Not if you do *exactly* as I say. Then it can't possibly fail!"

Dr X strode out of the underground control room, whistling cheerfully.

Plug looked at Socket and Socket looked at Plug. They both sighed.

"I have a bad feeling about this," said Socket.

Top Secret – Nessie-bot plans

Speed: 9/10

Travel mode: underwater

Special features:
* Camouflage to match the murky loch
* Powerful fins to cut through the water

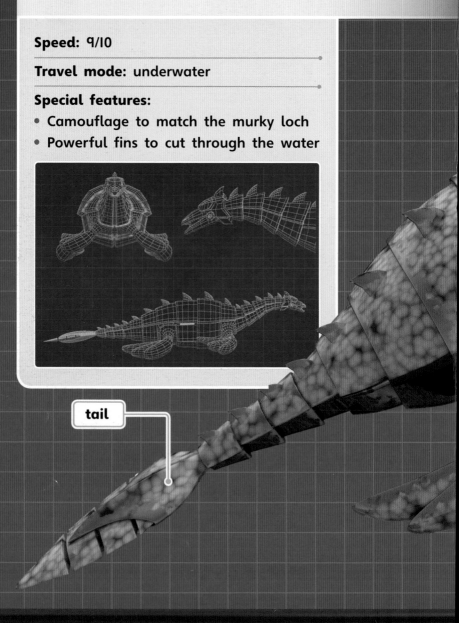

tail

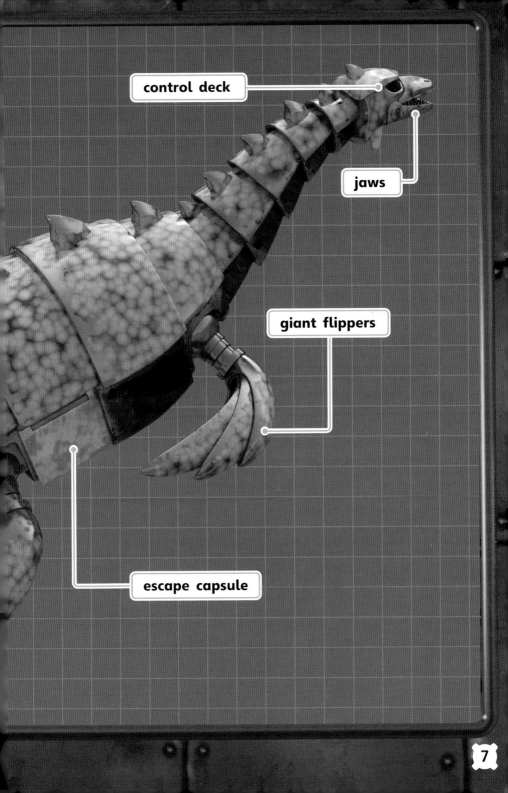

control deck

jaws

giant flippers

escape capsule

Chapter 2 – The micro submarine

Excited chatter filled the school bus. After weeks of looking forward to the trip, the children were finally on their way to Scotland.

"It's going to be great," said Ant, nudging Tiger for what seemed like the hundredth time. "I've been reading all about the Loch Ness monster and if we ..."

"I know," scowled Tiger. "You've told me. If we go out on the loch at the right time of day, there's a chance we might see it. *If* it existed, Ant."

Before Ant could argue back, Mrs Mills' voice cut through the chatter.

"Well, children, I hope you're all as excited as I am about this trip," she said. "There's going to be lots to do *and* we've got an extra-special treat lined up for you later." She paused. "I have a friend who is working at Loch Ness at the moment and he's agreed to talk to us about his scientific discoveries."

An enthusiastic murmur rippled down the coach.

"Oh, great!" muttered Tiger. "How is that *fun?*"

Ant beamed. "I'll be able to talk to him about Nessie! He's bound to know all about it. Did I tell you there were some sightings just last week?"

"Yes, Ant," sighed Tiger. "You've told me about a million times!"

Ant pretended not to hear. He didn't care what the others thought – Nessie was real and he was determined to prove it. He opened his book once again. He wanted to have all his facts ready when he talked to Mrs Mills' friend. Ant was sure he'd understand.

Nessie

Loch Ness is a large lake in the Highlands of Scotland. It is 230 metres deep – the second deepest lake in the country.

It is said to be home to the famous Loch Ness monster, affectionately known as Nessie.

Over the years there have been many reported sightings of Nessie. It was first brought to the world's attention in July 1933. A couple on holiday in Scotland claimed they saw the monster and their story was reported in the papers. Many more sightings followed.

In 1963, some film footage appeared to show the monster in the water. However, it was shot from a long way away and is very unclear. Something was in the water but whether it was a monster has not been proven.

Nessie 'facts'!

- The Loch Ness Monster's nickname is 'Nessie'.
- Nessie is believed to have a long neck and tail, a couple of humps and large flippers.
- The last reported sighting of Nessie was in November 2011.

Ant was still talking about Nessie when they arrived at the loch hours later. Huge hills framed the edges of the deep, dark lake and, standing on the shore, was Dr Sheldon Walker.

"Hi, everybody! Welcome to Loch Ness – one of the deepest lochs in Scotland," said Dr Walker. "It's *because* Loch Ness is so deep that I need some hi-tech gadgets to help me do my job," he said with a smile as he gestured to the water. There, bobbing on the surface, a micro-sub glistened in the sun.

Dr Walker pressed a button on the remote he was holding and the micro-sub whirred in the water near them. Playing with the controls, he made the craft glide through the water and then disappear beneath the surface.

"There are cameras on the sub which help me study all the creatures in the loch," explained Dr Walker. "If there's time, maybe a few of you could try steering it."

Before Dr Walker could say any more, Ant's hand shot up.

"You said you study *all* the creatures in the loch. "Does that mean you've seen Nessie?" asked Ant enthusiastically.

"Oh no, here we go again," groaned Tiger.

"You mean the monster?" said Dr Walker, smiling.

Ant nodded eagerly.

"Not so far," laughed Dr Walker kindly. "I think most scientists would agree that the Loch Ness monster is a myth."

Ant looked thoughtfully across the loch. If only there was some way to prove Nessie really did exist.

Tiger's voice interrupted his thoughts. "That micro-sub is so cool. I hope *I* get a chance to steer it."

A smile spread across Ant's face. He'd just had a brilliant idea of his own.

Chapter 3 – Underwater world

Ant's idea was simple. He wanted the others to shrink and climb into the micro-sub with him so they could use it to explore the loch – and find Nessie.

Max wasn't keen. "I don't know, Ant," he said. "It would be stealing, wouldn't it? What if it gets damaged?"

"It would only be *borrowing*," said Ant. "Besides, think how famous we'll be if we prove Nessie exists. We'll be legends. People will talk about us for centuries!"

"We'd have to explain how we did it, though," laughed Cat. She could see why Max was worried but she knew how important this was to Ant.

Ant looked at Max with a pleading expression.

"Oh, all right," Max said with a shrug. "I suppose it might be fun."

"We'll have to wait for the right moment," said Ant, taking charge. "We can't risk people seeing us shrink."

Fortunately, just then, Dr Walker came to their rescue, leading everyone away to look at one of his experiments. The four friends hung back from the rest of the group and waited.

Soon the four friends were all alone. They turned the dials on their watches and shrank to micro-size. They climbed through the micro-sub's hatch and found themselves standing on a small deck. Big windows stretched across the front, looking out into the murky depths of the loch.

Ant tried to work out how to control the sub. He eagerly started pressing buttons and pulling levers. Suddenly, the micro-sub shot forwards. The children stumbled as the sub started to dive into the murky depths of the loch.

The deeper they plunged, the darker it got.
"There must be some lights," said Cat,
sounding a little worried. Max flicked a switch
and two powerful beams cut through the gloom
ahead of them. Now they could see the steep
rocky walls of the loch. A shoal of fish darted
past the viewscreen.

"It looks like you're out of luck, Ant," said Max, after a few minutes of scouring the loch. "I think we should go back."

"Max is right," said Cat. "It's such a huge lake I doubt we'd be able to find anything in this tiny sub."

"We can't go back yet!" said Ant. "I'll never get this chance again."

"No, Ant," said Max, more firmly this time. "We need to get back before anyone notices the sub is missing."

"Hey, hang on a second," said Tiger. "What was that?"

Max, Cat and Ant whipped round in the direction Tiger was pointing. Their jaws dropped open.

Chapter 4 – Nessie-bot

Nobody moved. They all stared out of the window, unable to believe what was right in front of them.

Ant looked at his friends. "I can't believe it! We've found Nessie," he cheered.

Max, Cat and Tiger weren't smiling. Whatever it was, it was HUGE.

"We have to follow her," continued Ant. "This is my one chance to prove that Nessie isn't a myth."

Before the others had a chance to argue, Ant pressed a button and the sub shot forward.

"I'm serious, Ant," said Max. "We have to get this sub back. You've got five minutes and then we're heading for the shore."

Ant didn't answer. He pushed the micro-sub on, ignoring Max's warning.

The micro-sub surged forward. It began to gain steadily on the dark shape ahead. Soon they could see giant flippers and a long tail moving up and down in the water. The four friends turned to each other and grinned. They'd found Nessie!

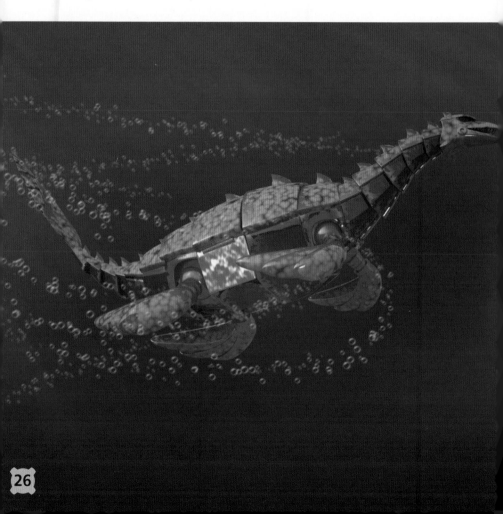

However, if the children had looked into the creature's eyes, they would have seen something very strange – Plug and Socket!

"They seem to have taken the bait, Boss," said Plug, talking to Dr X through the communication screen on the control deck.

Dr X chuckled with glee. "I *love* it when a plan comes together! You two *do* remember the rest of the plan, don't you?"

"There's more to the plan?" Socket asked.

Dr X sighed, then spoke very slowly. "You are to lead those irritating kids to an isolated part of the loch. There you will capture them. You will then bring them to me in the X-pod which will be waiting for you nearby. Got that?"

"Yes, Boss!" Plug and Socket said together.

"Just get on with it then!" said Dr X.

Then the screen went blank.

Chapter 5 – Enormous jaws

"Take the controls for a second, Max," Ant said suddenly. "I want to get some photos on my watch."

Max sighed. He wanted to get back to the surface as quickly as possible – taking photos would just slow them down.

"Actually, aren't there supposed to be cameras on here too?" asked Ant, when he'd finished. "I've got an idea. If we film Nessie on the sub's cameras, Dr Walker will *have* to take us seriously. Tiger, quick, find the camera controls."

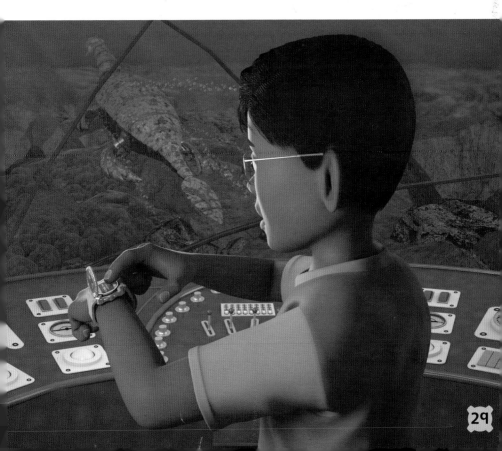

"We need to head back, Ant," urged Cat. "We'll soon be missed."

"Just a few more seconds," answered Ant, not really listening.

"I don't like where your monster is leading us, Ant," continued Cat. "The loch seems to be a lot darker here."

"Hang on," said Tiger. "I think Nessie's slowing down."

The others peered into the darkness. The monster *was* slowing down and it was turning round as well. In no time at all, it was facing the micro-sub, its huge flippers gently moving up and down in the water.

"Er, I think it's coming towards us …" Tiger said uneasily as Nessie headed straight for them.

It was soon dangerously close.

The micro-sub rocked in the water as the monster opened its enormous jaws. The four friends looked at the huge 'creature' staring at them.

"Hey!" shouted Tiger. "There are people in its eyes! No, it can't be … It's Dr X's henchmen. It's not Nessie at all. It's a trap!"

Tiger was right. Plug and Socket were smiling and waving at them through the fake monster's eyes!

"Quick! Turn round!" said Cat.

"Hold on," cried Ant, already spinning the sub around.

CLANG! The Nessie-bot's enormous jaws slammed shut, only just missing the micro-sub.

The tiny craft shuddered in the ripples of the water. Ant shoved the controls forward and the sub shot down towards the bottom of the loch. The Nessie-bot followed.

"It's still behind us, Ant," said Cat.

Ant pushed another lever on the control panel and the sub shot up. Again, the Nessie-bot stayed on their tail. Whatever Ant did, the robotic creature stayed right behind them, its jaws snapping.

"You can't let them catch us, Ant!" said Cat.

"I've got an idea," said Max. "It might be our only chance …"

33

Chapter 6 – The last second

"Ant, turn the sub round. Aim left," Max ordered.

"Hang on, everyone!" Ant yelled as he forced the micro-sub to change direction. As it was only supposed to be remote-controlled, it wasn't easy to steer the tiny sub.

The Nessie-bot followed, snapping at their tail.

"We're going in the wrong direction!" shouted Cat. "We're heading straight for the side of the loch. That's just solid rock, not an escape route!"

"Exactly," said Max. "I'm hoping Dr X's men will be too busy watching us to see the danger ahead. Brace yourself, everyone!"

"If we're going to swerve, there's not much time left," shouted Cat. The rock wall was dead ahead. It loomed over them so all they could see was rock.

"Whatever you're going to do, Max, you need to do it soon!" cried Tiger.

"We've got to leave it to the very last second," Max said, his face determined.

"We don't have long!" muttered Tiger. "Three … two …"

"Now, Ant!" Max yelled.

Ant pulled back the controls. The micro-sub flew up through the water, scraping its underside along the rock wall.

CRASH! The Nessie-bot smashed into the side of the loch. It hit the rocks head on and crumpled like a paper bag. The broken remains slid down into the depths of the loch – lost in the darkness.

Chapter 7 – Mysterious shadow

Max, Cat, Ant and Tiger looked at each other. None of them spoke.

Eventually Cat broke the silence. "Do you think Dr X's men are OK? I hope they aren't hurt."

Without answering, Ant turned the micro-sub around and guided it down to look at the wreck.

Clouds of sand blurred their vision but they kept going. They had to see if the crew of the Nessie-bot was OK.

As they got closer to the wreck, a small craft darted through the beam of the sub's headlights.

"That was an escape capsule," said Max. "I think they're fine. Let's have a quick check to make sure and then we need to get this sub back before anything else happens."

Ant looked sheepish. "Sorry. If I hadn't dragged you down here, this wouldn't have happened. I really thought we'd found Nessie."

"I know, Ant," said Cat gently. "It would have been cool if we really *had* found Nessie." She smiled. "Now let's just get back to the surface quickly and hope no one has noticed we're missing."

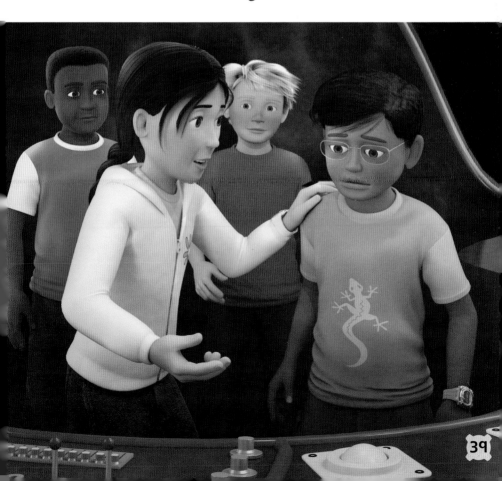

Minutes later, the four friends stepped back on to dry land. They turned the dials on their watches and grew back to normal size. They quickly joined the rest of the class and boarded the bus back home.

Ant took a last, lingering look at the loch as the bus moved away. It had been a strange and disappointing day.

Back at NASTI, Dr X was disappointed as well. In fact, he was *furious*. Plug and Socket stood in front of him, wincing and twitching, as he shouted at them.

"I don't believe it!" Dr X yelled. "I couldn't have *made* it any easier!"

"Sorry, Boss, but those kids can be very crafty," said Plug.

"Yeah, they do so much dodging they make you dizzy," said Socket.

"Stop, stop!" yelled Dr X. "I can't bear it any more."

He strode out of the control room, muttering under his breath about irritating children, hapless henchmen and his watches, his precious, precious watches.

Back in Greenville, Ant wasn't in the mood for company. He left the others and went home to download the pictures from his watch. Even if they hadn't seen Nessie today he still clung to the belief that she did exist.

The computer whirred as the photos slowly downloaded.

Download complete.

That's strange, Ant thought, squinting at the first image. He clicked on the next … and the next.

In each one there was a dark, mysterious shape lurking behind the metallic monster.

"I knew it …" Ant said to himself. He smiled. "I think I'll keep you to myself this time, though."

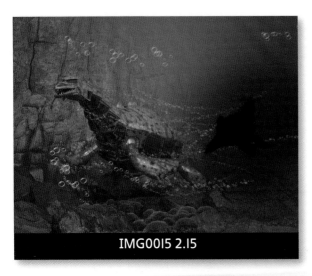

IMG0015 2.15

IMG0016 2.16

That evening, Dr Walker also had a surprise. As he packed up the micro-sub, he discovered a file waiting to be downloaded. He couldn't explain it – he was sure the memory disk had been empty that morning. What he found on the film was even more unbelievable. He reached for his phone – he had to share his amazing discovery right away. Would people believe him, though?

LOCH NESS NEWS

'SCIENTIST FINDS EVIDENCE OF LOCH NESS MONSTER!'

Dr Sheldon Walker claims to have found evidence that the famous Loch Ness Monster – long thought to be a myth – actually exists.

"I use a small robot submarine to explore Loch Ness and I found this amazing film footage on the camera. The submarine was also damaged. It looked like it had been attacked by something large with sharp teeth. I have never believed in the myth but this new evidence has made me change my mind!"

Other scientists have commented that Dr Walker must be mistaken.

Renowned scientist is convinced Nessie exists.

Find out more ...

Read about Team X's adventures in the City of Troy in *The Trojan Horse*.

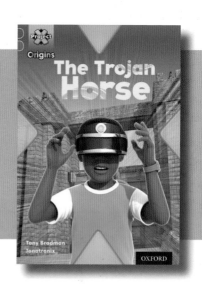

Who is Tiger's top legendary hero? Find out in *Tiger's Legendary Heroes*.